Animals Mourn for Da Leopard

AND OTHER WEST
AFRICAN TALES

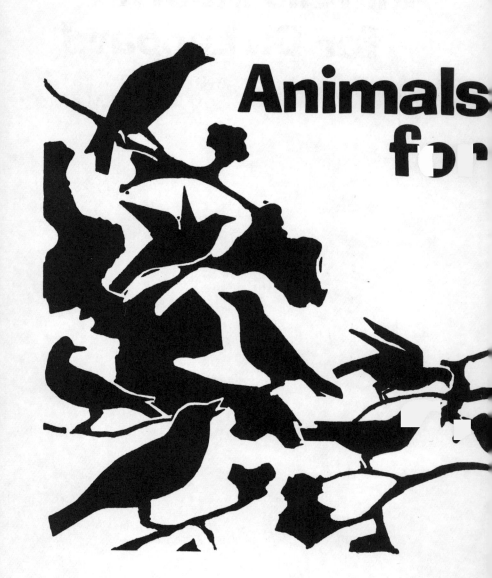

Animals fo'

PETER G. DORLIAE

Mourn Da Leopard

AND OTHER WEST AFRICAN TALES

Illustrated by S. Irein Wangboje

THE BOBBS-MERRILL COMPANY, INC.

Indianapolis   New York

The Bobbs-Merrill Company, Inc.
A Subsidiary of Howard W. Sams & Co., Inc.
Publishers Indianapolis Kansas City New York
Text copyright © 1970 by Peter G. Dorliae
Illustrations copyright © 1970 by S. Irein Wangboje
Designed by Judith Lerner
Printed in the United States of America
All rights reserved
Library of Congress catalog card number: 74-84167
First edition

Acknowledgment: NO ONE SUCCEEDS
in life without the help of others in his vicinity.
Many persons assisted me in the compilation of this book,
but none more than Mrs. Edna W. Chandler, wife of a
former U.S. AID official, Dr. J. O. Chandler, who lived
in Liberia for some years.

I sincerely register my gratefulness to Mrs. Chandler
for her invaluable services in bringing this book to reality.
Also to my messenger, Sergeant Kei Doukpa, I say
many thanks for his masterful telling of stories,
some of which are included herein.

PETER G. DORLIAE

Contents

Animals Mourn for Da Leopard

AND OTHER WEST AFRICAN TALES

DA LEOPARD

I: Animals Mourn
for Da Leopard

FROM the time of the first creation Da Leopard has been greatly feared by all other animals. They have good reason to fear him. For Da Leopard chases them and eats them.

This went on for many, many years. At last the animals came together to protect themselves from Da Leopard. They hid themselves in a sloping valley between mountains. They felt that together they could enjoy the last part of their lives in some security in a place hidden from Da Leopard.

Da Leopard knew they were hiding from him, and he searched and searched for them. He watched and looked between jungles and thickets but did not find them.

Oldman Spider, who is always roving around and hunting, one day came upon the animals in their place of safety. He cried bitterly to show them that he missed them and told them he was sorry they must always stay in hiding from Da Leopard.

You see, Oldman Spider is a friend to any living thing, but the only obstacle about him is that one cannot depend upon him. He usually puts himself on the side of the stronger one. If a strong one shows he is weakening, Oldman Spider will go to the other side. He may let a man down at the beginning, the middle, or the close of business.

The animals were not used to Mr. Spider's tricks, and so they mingled with him with a whole heart. Also they liked him very much for his fun-making ability.

The animals organized what they called a "safety dance," which took place every evening before they went to bed. They appointed Oldman Spider leader of the safety dance in the valley. Every evening he called them together to enjoy this hilarious social gathering.

One day he asked for leave to go to his home to tell his family what he was doing and to let them know he was safe. The animals granted him leave but urged him to return quickly for they would miss him.

But, mind you, he did not go home! He went to find Da Leopard.

He knew where Da Leopard was, and that Da Leopard was hungry and looking for these animals.

Oldman Spider himself cannot manage to kill animals like the Wild Hog, Buffalo, Hippopotamus, and other dangerous animals. But Da can. Whenever Da Leopard destroyed an animal, he would give Oldman Spider some meat. So Oldman Spider brought Da Leopard to the foot of the mountain and said to him, "Please lie down still and play you are dead. I am going to call those stupid animals."

Da Leopard did as Oldman Spider directed. Oldman Spider placed a rotten crab under Leopard and the scent was as strong as if Da Leopard were truly dead.

Then Oldman Spider advised Da Leopard thus: "Be patient until the animals gather in great quantity. These animals here—Squirrel and Antelope especially—are tricky and they will be around you, too. But you are fine and strong and you will know how to watch them. But be sure you remember that we shall divide equally the animals you shall kill."

Oldman Spider made his way into the midst of the animals, crying great crocodile tears and saying, "Do you not smell the odor of death in this place? Da Leopard is dead. No one comes to be sorry for him. Let us forget the past and go to bury whomever has done wrong to us. I come to appeal to your good hearts. Forget about his ungratefulness to us. Hard-hearted men at war shoot one another, yet they bury their dead. Are they better than we? Are they more sensible than we? Please follow me. Let's bury the damn Da Leopard before he spoils our forest with his rotten body. If we don't, his bones might remain on our soil, especially his wicked and dangerous teeth. You know that even touching his teeth might be our end."

Oldman Spider made this misleading speech and all the animals believed him, every word he said. Man has brains for thinking and still he forgets. So why shouldn't dumb animals forget?

After Oldman Spider's powerful speech those stupid animals followed him to attend Da Leopard's funeral services. Every animal cried mournfully and uncontrollably to show that Da Leopard was one of them.

Squirrel and Antelope sat off to one side and cried in a low and alluding voice: "We did not hear about Da's illness. He killed Porcupine only three days ago. How come he died so quickly? Did he dided a heart break?"

Oldman Spider did not like these comments.

6

LOBSTER WENT CLOSER TO THE SO-CALLED DEAD BODY

He tried to get rid of Squirrel and Antelope saying, "You are little children. Do not cry here, or you will get fever from crying." He went here and there consoling the other mourners. When he passed Da's body he lay down and warned Da, "The children are doing bad-o-o-o! Make haste and start operation on these bitches—m-m-m-"

Now, Lobster, who had come to visit his cousin Scorpion, had heard Oldman Spider's words earlier and went along to take part in the funeral procession. Lobster knew that Leopard's tail tip should rest on the ground if Leopard was really dead. Lobster saw that the tip of Da Leopard's tail kept touching the ground in a most regular manner, rising up slowly and each time falling down again.

Once long ago Oldman Spider and Otter had played certain tricks on Fish. Lobster was one of the survivors of those tricks. He had seen them. So now Lobster determined to watch well and test Da Leopard.

Unknown to the mourners and Oldman Spider, Lobster went closer to the so-called dead body and tickled the anus with his sharp pointed fingers.

The dead body quivered like the leaves of a tree standing in the middle of a river with a strong current. The second trip of Lobster's fingers caused the "dead" body to open its eyes an inch or so. The eyes looked at Lobster who continued tickling the "deceased" rascal.

By this time the timid animals noticed what Lobster was doing. They stopped crying abruptly, but kept sobbing. They looked with serious faces. Oldman Spider said it was a very disrespectful way for Lobster to treat a dead body.

Suddenly the animals saw a faint movement in the corpse. The animal mourners were seized first with unrest, then with fear.

Oldman Spider saw the change in behavior of the animals. He followed their glances and saw Lobster in action. He shouted at him to stop playing with a dead beast.

The frightened animals commenced leaving one by one. But Da Leopard, urged on by Oldman Spider, managed to kill a few of them before they got away.

Then the two friends, Da Leopard and Oldman Spider, fell into a quarrel over the division of the meat. They parted in anger with each other, leaving much of it to rot where it was.

MR. SPIDER BUILT A GREAT FIRE BENEATH THE MOUNTAIN
WHERE THE HOLE OPENED

2: Mr. Spider Smokes Out the World's Hole

ALL living things created by God were locked up in Mount Tonva (Big Mountain). Even the African country devils, seen in one form or another, were locked up in there.

God did not choose to tell man what types of beings were inside Big Mountain. All man could do was allow his curiosity to carry him into guessing games. Sometimes traces of footprints were seen at the base of the mountain. Then the guessing would become active again.

"Did you see the great footprints made last night?" one would ask his neighbor.

"Yes, I saw some in the sand at the waterside."

During the season when male animals go hunting and fighting for females, they made fearful drumming sounds. The noise of the drumming sounded all through the bush. The people shook with fear whenever the drumming sounds were heard.

"We must go from here!" they said. "Animals that leave such great tracks and make such fearful noise must be very dangerous indeed!"

No one really wanted to leave, for it was their town. Also, it was not too hard to find meat there. If anyone really needed meat he could easily find opossums or small rats—as many as he needed.

But fear of the big animals in the mountain grew, as fear of things unseen and unknown always grows—that is, until something or someone takes the veil away and reveals the secret.

"Let us pray to God, and all gods, to tell us about these big animals and tell us how to deal with them," said one.

"We could smoke them out of their holes," said another. "We might find so much meat we would not need to hunt for small rats any more."

Man seldom smoked out the small animals since he got enough of them without doing so. But to smoke out the world's Creation Hole and bring forth big, unknown animals—that was something great. No one quite dared to do it.

At a time when there was much discussion and fear about what huge monsters might be within Mount Tonva, Mr. Spider came along.

Everyone knows that Mr. Spider is not only tricky and hard-headed, but he is a world vagabond as well. He goes here and there, never staying long in one place, always looking for relatives who might feed him.

He remembered his tenth cousin who lived in the region of Mount Tonva and decided to visit him.

Almost the first news he was told was about the animal treasure inside the Big Mountain.

A plan came at once into the hard head of Mr. Spider, but he told no one about it. He went out every morning to cut big wood sticks to smoke out big meat animals in the world's Hole.

"Where do you go every morning, Cousin Spider?" his tenth cousin asked. "It is not like you to work so much."

"I am going to smoke out opossums," he said. "I hear that there are many fat opossums around this town. I am very hungry for fat opossum meat."

"Very well," his tenth cousin answered. "Do as you will."

Day after day Mr. Spider worked, bringing wood that he knew would burn fast and hot.

Early one fine morning, Mr. Spider built a great fire beneath the mountain where the Hole opened out. The mountain seemed to burst into flames while smoke curled over the top of it.

The town people awoke and saw the smoke, but they did not force sleep from their eyes. They thought it was the volcano that boiled out and came down the mountain almost every morning.

Animals large and animals small jumped and ran and hopped madly from the mountain. This confusion was much greater than trouble-maker Mr. Spider had expected. Bewildered and scared, Mr. Spider looked for spaces to jump into to escape the animals' horns and big feet. He jumped here and there, but each time he jumped to the space he had selected, some big animal had beat him to it!

A group of tall country devils stood over him and frightened Mr. Spider even more. So, instead of killing any of the big meat animals as he had planned to do, Mr. Spider gave up and ran away.

At last, the drowsy people of this mountain realized that the smoke did not come from the volcano. Now the people came awake! They were terrified when animals of many strange types came running and jumping into their fenced town.

Men and women whose joints were stiff from sleeping began to run from the giant creatures. And the creatures ran from the people! Lions, bush cows, tigers, leopards, and other fierce animals dashed here and there. At last, they went off into the bush. In time, they quieted down and made homes there.

Some, like the cows, sheep, and goats, did not run so wildly and fast. They were later captured and tamed by man.

And that is the way the world's Creation Hole was smoked out, the way animals first came into the earth world and found homes here.

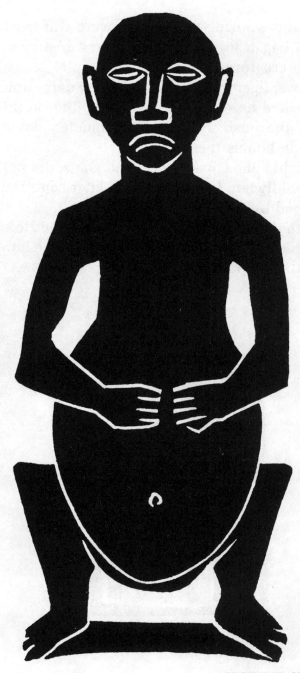

PRESIDENT STOMACH

3: "We Oppose President Stomach!"

WHEN God created man, he made the Stomach, Heart, Head, Hands, Feet, Eyes, Nose, and other parts of the body. He made Stomach the President and Heart the Secretary. God advised all parts of the body to respect and obey President Stomach.

Each part was given certain work to do. Feet stand up; Eyes see; Hands hold, cut, and grab; Nose smells; and Mouth chews while Throat swallows. President Stomach keeps all things that enter the body.

It happened on one occasion that these parts of the body began to feel jealous and said that they were working hard for Stomach alone and getting no benefit from it.

Throat said, "Gentlemen, all the food you give me does not spend a minute with me. I think Stomach ties twine to it and hauls it down to himself. Let us elect a new president and do away with Stomach."

"We chew the food, but Stomach takes it in and enjoys it alone. If you don't vote against this president, we—I especially—will leave and go to stay in a foreign country," said Teeth.

"Your situation is better than ours," said Eyes. "For us, we simply see the food, but do not touch it. As for you, Friend Throat, it does pass through you."

Now Feet wished to speak. He said, "We think we are like the monkey in the saying, 'Monkey works, baboon draws.' We only walk to the food, but never get anything.

"Let us go to God and tell him that we do not want President Stomach; he is greedy and never cares for us."

They all agreed to do this.

So, these parts of man sent a delegation to God and said, "We oppose President Stomach."

God asked them if they knew what they were talking about.

Nose jumped up and said, "We are human beings whom you made, Papa. We know what

18

we are talking about. If you will kill us, do so now. But we do not want President Stomach. Look, he even resembles a lady's bag which takes in everything!"

"Do not abuse him, else you will be ashamed to look at his face in the future," God warned.

God told them to go back home and decide whom they wanted for president. He told them that before and after the meeting they must not eat anything; otherwise President Stomach will still make use of their labor.

All of them turned back with gladness saying, "He thinks he is the only man created by God. Let us show him we can do without him!"

"I am glad the Oldman said we must not give him anything to eat," said Throat.

God had promised to meet with them in two days. So they selected Mouth to be their spokesman. They sang and said, "Shame on him, down with President Stomach!"

On the morning that God was to come, these opposition gentlemen had not eaten for two days and each man was half trembling with hunger.

They asked Left Eye to be the president, but Left Eye said, "I cannot see well since yesterday. How can I be a president?"

Left Foot was asked to be the president, but he refused and said, "I cannot stand upright due to hunger. What part of me looks like a president?"

When all had refused to be president, Spokesman Mouth said, "It's better that we bring Stomach back as our president because he has more room to keep things. Who are Throat and Nose to lead us?"

At the end, God asked them to bring in the name of the candidate they wanted. But none of them had ever agreed to act as president. They brought in the name of Stomach and said, "Lord, please make Stomach our king and not president. We see now that he divides our daily food equally. We did not realize this until the last two days."

God told them not to make a big mouth against Stomach again.

And God ordered the Hands to cook soft rice to give it to King Stomach that he might strengthen the others. This was done, and after thirty minutes Eyes began to see well; Feet were jumping up and down; Mouth started to talk louder. All of them became their natural selves again. Now they sang another song, a very different one.

"Shame on us, shame on us! We support King Stomach. He will be our king forever!"

MONKEY CHALLENGES SNAIL TO A RACE

4: The Monkey and the Snail

ON a hot summer day a big monkey called Gro came across a snail named Drinn crawling along the forest path.

Gro, who was a known boaster, sat still and watched the slow movement of Drinn. After a while he asked, "Do you like it, this manner of walking? How long will it take you to get where you are going?" Saying this, Gro laughed and went home.

The next morning he met Drinn at another place on the path.

"Have you no foot? Nothing but a hard coat?" he asked.

"Leave me, this is what I was created with," said the snail.

Gro started to laugh again.

"Can you take a running race with me?" he asked.

"Yes, I can take a running race with you," answered Drinn, "even with the cheetah in the bush."

It is well known that the cheetah, first brother to the leopard, is a fast-running animal. The idea of a race between the cheetah and the snail was beyond thinking. Gro found the whole matter very amusing. He laughed again.

"When shall we start our race, lazy snail?" he asked.

"It is up to you, Mr. Boaster. You must set the date for our race," Drinn answered.

Gro set the race for Wednesday morning.

On Wednesday morning, Gro and Drinn came to the starting point. Gro stood for a while, joking, boasting, and mocking Drinn. Then he shouted, and the race began.

Gro, being sure of winning the race and knowing that Drinn was slow, ran backward for a mile, saying, "Who is Drinn, to win over me in a running race? Let me give him a chance to go further."

They were to stop at six different stations to see if each man was still in the race. Gro called at the first station and Drinn answered him on the spot. Gro was surprised to meet Drinn there.

Gro became serious and made up his mind to run faster, to leave Drinn behind. He hurried, jumping from tree to tree. Sometimes he missed a branch and landed on the ground. He covered five of the stations. At every station he reached he met Drinn. No matter how fast he ran, Drinn was ahead of him.

The palms of his hands swelled up and hurt so badly that at last he gave up to the snail.

"My friend," he said, "I salute you. I thought you were a very slow creature. I boasted for nothing. See how my body hurts."

Drinn then told Gro his secret for winning the race.

"You boasted too much. That is why I planned this way to make you ashamed. I kept my seat and never moved anywhere. I hired friends to help me. I placed one friend at each point we were to meet to answer whenever you called. I remained right in this spot while you almost killed yourself, running and jumping. Sometimes a race is won with the head, not the feet!"

Tired and almost sick, Gro repeated his salute. Drinn answered the salute, and they parted.

IT IS NOT EASY TO CARRY A GROWN PERSON IN A
HAMMOCK OVER A SLIPPERY PATH

5: Farmer Zia, the Hard-Luck Man

ZIA was a well-known native farmer. His people loved him dearly for the hard work he did. Every year he led a group of farmers who visited and worked on each man's farm. Such a group is called a koo.

Zia and his group of men went to a farm one Wednesday morning to fell trees. It was the time of the year when bush must be cut to make the land ready for rice farms. People came from near and far to praise Zia for his steady working ways.

Young girls and boys followed the farmers to sing and to eat the lavish food prepared by the owners of the farms. After lunch hours, the farmers returned to their day's work.

One of the farmers, known as Kago, had cut his tree on one side but forgot to tell the others to look out for a falling tree.

As Zia, the chief farmer, was jumping here and there in his happy way of working, Kago finished cutting the tree. It fell on Farmer Zia!

The people rushed from all directions to save Zia, the master farmer. His nose was bleeding badly and he was suffering. Many people put their hands under the log and lifted it, while others dragged Zia free of the log.

By mistake they set Zia on a freshly cut stump. A very sharp stick stuck out from the stump and went through his left leg. He screamed with great pain.

"You are killing me!" he shouted. "You saved me from the log. You kill me with another stick!"

Zia's wife and children and many others present burst into tears. The people called for a hammock seat to carry Zia to the village. A two-man hammock frame was prepared to carry Zia home to take medicine.

"Take your time," said one farmer friend. "There was rain last night. The ground is slippery."

It is not easy, even for two strong men, to

carry a grown person in a hammock over a slippery path. As the two men carried the hammock up a small hill, the front man stumbled and dropped his part of the hammock. Zia and the hammock fell on a stone, which broke his backbone!

Seeing this new misfortune, men and women following the hammock again burst into crying. Someone carried the news ahead into their village. Many people came to sympathize with Zia and his family.

The hammock men again took the wounded man to the house where Doctor Madein, native healer, was expected to meet him.

The door sash below the house into which Zia was to be carried was too high. The back hammock man stepped in the hole below the sash and stumbled. This suddenly pushed the front hammock man against the rice dryer that hung from the ceiling. A piece of bamboo on the dryer struck Zia's eye. Poor Zia screamed and groaned.

When this happened most of the people stopped crying because the tragedies had been too many. But Zia's grandmother, who was still crying like a child, hastily grabbed a cup to dip water and to wash his face. There was pounded pepper in the cup, but she did not see it.

Zia's grandmother washed his sore, cut face.

It burned, it hurt, and Zia again screamed louder and louder.

"Again you try to kill me!" he screamed. "Even my own grandmother makes me suffer too much!"

All the calm sympathizers were puzzled about why so many bad things can happen to one man, in so short a time—one bad thing after another!

The people said, "Poor Zia! He is a bad-luck man. Dr. Madein must make strong medicine, or he will not be cured of his misfortunes."

"Let us suggest to Dr. Madein to use the swampy heating method, that Zia's blood may circulate before applying real medicine," others said.

The doctor agreed, and a long grave-like hole was dug in the swamp. Zia was placed lengthwise in the hole and covered with dirt. Only his face was left uncovered. A great fire was built over him for the heat to help his blood circulation. Then he was given proper treatment by Dr. Madein.

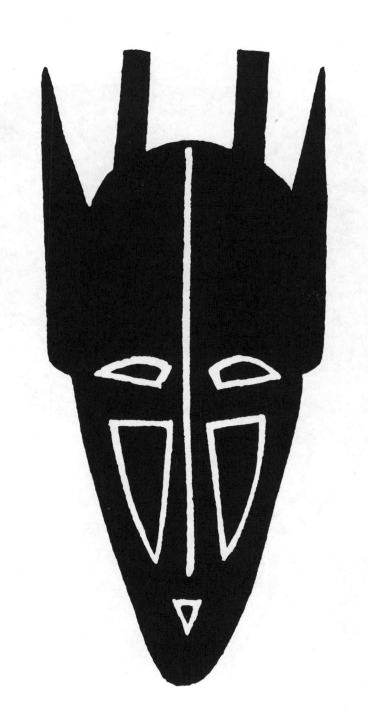

DR. SPIDER

6: The City Mortician and Dr. Spider

A strong friendship existed between Dr. Spider and Pa Elephant. It was even said to be a holy friendship, for they promised to die on the same day.

Everyone in the vicinity knew about this death promise. When Dr. Spider complained of headache they knew Pa Elephant, too, would have a headache. If Pa Elephant suffered from diarrhea, Dr. Spider would also be ill from it.

One day Pa Elephant decided to go up country, far away from the city.

"I will return soon," he told his friend, Dr. Spider. "I only want to get away from the city

33

for a while."

But he did not come back. In a very short time (as bad news travels fast) word came that Pa Elephant was dead. He had slept on the floor and an ant bit him on his trunk. The trunk swelled inside and outside. The inside swelling shut off his breath, and thus he died.

Relatives, friends, and well-wishers went to the village where Pa Elephant had died. Dr. Spider, of course, was with the big crowd going up country. He was very worried and talked to himself all the way.

"Why did my friend Elephant visit this country town? He knew he would be sleeping on the floor where ants sometimes crawl. Was this the kind of death we promised to die? Will there be an ant there to bite me also? If there is no ant, must I die anyway, in some other horrible manner? Husband and wife usually die at separate times. Not so? Why must two men die the same day, when God, who knows, did not say so?"

Dr. Spider kept asking himself these questions just to avoid dying with his friend, as he had promised.

When they reached the village nearly everyone went into the hut to see the body of Pa Elephant. But Dr. Spider did not go in.

Because human and animal bodies spoil very fast in hot countries, Pa Elephant's body was very far gone and was swollen to a great size.

When time came for the burial, Dr. Spider saw his friend's huge, swollen body for the first time. But he did not realize why his friend's body was big in size. Another thought came to his mind. Dr. Spider had always been a great glutton, thinking of food above all things.

"Oh!" he said to himself, "My friend has become very fat. His family has given him much food. His friends have treated him well."

Now he thought that dying might be very pleasant, if he could be fed as he thought Pa Elephant had been.

"As coma is a sleep before death," he said, "if I die and see that my family do not care for me, I can come out of the coma if I am not fed."

After Pa Elephant was buried, all his relatives and friends returned to the city. Dr. Spider returned with the others.

At next daybreak, and with no word to anyone, Dr. Spider began shouting in one long, screaming shout, holding his breath to appear dead at the same time.

Many people heard this most unusual noise and came running to Dr. Spider's place.

Dr. Spider lay quite still in his spider coma, hoping someone would bring food to him.

No one had ever done such a thing so it was not done now. Much food was brought, but it was given to the visiting strangers and other mourners. People thought Dr. Spider was truly dead.

"Come," they said, "let us not waste our time. This gentleman died as he said he would when Pa Elephant died. We have spent much of our time at Pa Elephant's wake. We cannot take more time for another wake just now. Let us bury Dr. Spider at once. A wake is not necessary. Like his friend, he is dead!"

Hearing these things, Dr. Spider, still in coma, became very worried. He began to talk to himself.

"You people in this city have often stirred up hatred against me. Since my death, not one of you has brought me even a piece of cassava. Yet, you want to bury me now! Whether this will happen or not, God only can tell!"

A city mortician named Gaveneh, a man of the Bassa tribe, was called to take care of the body. Preparations for burying Dr. Spider were going along fast and well.

Men and women in black suits and dresses were forming into a funeral procession. Bunches of flowers were brought to the building where the body lay. As soon as Gaveneh, the mortician, came, the funeral would begin. But Gaveneh was busy and sent one of his boys to put white clothes on the body and pre-

36

pare it for burial.

When Dr. Spider saw Gaveneh's boy, he thought of a way to escape death and burial. The body said, "You are only one of Gaveneh's small boys. Please go away. This dead body's teeth might bite you, and you know a dead body's teeth are very dangerous. Let Gaveneh himself come to clothe me. He is a good mortician. He did well with my friend Elephant's body. He buried my mother some years ago and she did not return."

It is well known that if a mortician does not do his work well, a dead body can return in a new and dangerous form.

Gaveneh's boy did not stay to argue with the body. He ran as fast as he could to report to Gaveneh.

When Gaveneh heard the boy's frightening story he said, "Do not tell anyone about this. You hear? I will take care of this body myself."

Gaveneh walked to the funeral service building and went immediately to the body. He clothed the body carefully and did not hear it speak. But when he lowered the lid of the coffin Dr. Spider became very desperate. He pushed the lid open and began fighting Gaveneh.

"Ah-ha!" said Gaveneh, "so it is the clever Dr. Spider who vowed he would die when his friend died. He tries to pretend he is dead so he will be honored for his loyalty. Truly he will be honored, for he will be buried now. Gaveneh does such things very nicely, for it is his way to earn money. Gaveneh is a skilled mortician—very skilled indeed!"

Dr. Spider had no strength to talk back. He used all his energy to fight. But Gaveneh was the stronger and finally subdued the clever Dr. Spider.

Gaveneh called his boys to carry the coffin outside.

They carried it to the head of the procession, which was very long and in double lines. Friends of the late Pa Elephant were there also. Everyone walked slowly and sadly to the deep, sorrowful tones of the funeral drums.

Suddenly—no one could ever explain how—the coffin lid sprang open and Dr. Spider jumped out.

The fight began again, with Gaveneh's boys trying desperately to get the body back into the coffin.

Dr. Spider is a rascal man who had left his own family to suffer through life as best they could. So now no one came forth to help him.

But no one helped Gaveneh either. They were too scared! The procession lines broke up, and people ran for their lives. They said the dead body was catching anyone it could to go along with it. A dead-body scene is very dangerous, and people never want to stay in an area with such a thing. They ran far off and watched the grave from a distance.

When Gaveneh and his helpers, still chasing Dr. Spider, reached the seven-foot-deep grave, they were very tired.

Dr. Spider noticed their tiredness so he pretended he was dying a real death.

Gaveneh said, "We have him now. Let us rest for a moment and then we will finish this burying business."

Gaveneh drew a deep breath for resting.

Dr. Spider saw this. He gathered his energy for one last trial. He jumped into the nearby bush and disappeared. No one followed. It is no use to chase after a spider in the bush.

SAYE-DUO SAW A HOLLOWED-OUT LOG WITH STRANGE-
LOOKING WHITE EGGS AND HE WAS AFRAID

7: Mr. Spider and the Death Eggs

ONCE upon a time when Mr. Spider went hunting, he took a young boy, Saye-Duo, with him. Saye-Duo was glad to go along.

Because he was so young, he still had many things to learn. He knew that Mr. Spider was very clever and could no doubt teach him much about how to hunt.

Far into the forest they went, but saw no game. No deer were about, no birds, not even small woodrats. It was a bad day for hunting meat.

Mr. Spider and Saye-Duo started homeward with Saye-Duo walking ahead. Suddenly, at the side of the road, Saye-Duo saw a hollowed-out log with strange-looking white eggs in it.

Saye-Duo had never seen such eggs, and he was afraid. They were boa constrictor eggs, which were highly prized and very delicious, but he did not know this. He screamed at the top of his voice.

The scream frightened Mr. Spider, who began running toward the thick bush.

Saye-Duo soon had calmed his fear, for the eggs seemed to be quite harmless. He called to Mr. Spider.

"Come," he said, "I have found something strange here—many things, but they are not moving. I do not think they will hurt us. Come and see!"

Mr. Spider came to the hollow log and saw the eggs. He could not say at once what kind of eggs they were, but eggs were food. And whenever a matter of food comes to his attention, Mr. Spider thinks very fast.

He said, "Saye-Duo, you have found something very strange. These eggs may be filled with good medicine, or they may be filled with bad medicine. I will try to find out. In the meantime, we must not talk about these eggs when we get back to the village. If we do, the two of us will not see the coming of Easter. We will die before our time!"

The young boy was very frightened by Mr. Spider's words. He felt himself crying inside, and his body shook as with a chill and fever. He could not find the words to say yes or no before Mr. Spider spoke again.

"We have a great task before us," Mr. Spider said. "It may be very serious. People who see such wonderful eggs should not go into town together. They must go separately to their homes. You go on home now. I will come soon. But first I must go into the bush to get my headache treatment. My poor head gives me much pain lately."

Saye-Duo was glad to go home. Every moment he became more and more frightened about the strange eggs.

Mr. Spider watched Saye-Duo run away and disappear. Then he turned toward the bush, laughing softly to himself.

Soon he returned with a basket. Carefully he put the eggs into the basket and went back to his home in the village. He went a long way around so he would not be seen.

When night came he made a small cooking fire behind his house and cooked some of the eggs.

He had just begun to eat them when Saye-Duo came along.

Saye-Duo saw that Mr. Spider was eating

something round. Could it be one of the strange eggs they had seen in the hollow log? If those eggs were good to eat then he, Saye-Duo, should have his part! Oh, that clever and wicked Mr. Spider!

Saye-Duo ran to Telu, his mother, and told her the story.

Mother Telu listened well. Because she was a clever woman she knew what Saye-Duo must do.

"First, you must say nothing about what has happened. Tell no one at all. For if Mr. Spider hears that you have seen him eating some of the eggs he may hide the remainder. Or he may tell more lies, which will get plenty of trouble for us. I know something we can do."

And, wasting no time at all, she did it. She dug up some black dirt in the backyard of her hut. She rubbed it on one side of her son. She laid him in the middle of her front yard. Then she began to cry.

"Listen, my people! Listen to me! Mr. Spider carried my son into the forest where he saw 'death eggs.' Oh, my people! The boy is dying now. One side of him has become black with death color."

People came running to Telu and her son. Mr. Spider came, too.

Mr. Spider said, "I told your son not to open

his eyes wide in the forest. Yet he did so."

This was another of Mr. Spider's lies, for he had given no such warning to Saye-Duo.

Now Mr. Spider became very restless and worried. He knew that sooner or later the people would know how he had tricked Saye-Duo.

He rushed home and put all the remaining eggs back in the basket. Then he took water in his mouth to wash away the pieces of egg from between his teeth.

Again, he ran to look at Saye-Duo.

Telu had told her son to act weak and stupid until the egg palaver should be finished.

So, when Mr. Spider came with the basket of eggs, Saye-Duo was acting very weak and strange.

Mr. Spider set the basket of eggs before Telu and said, "Here is your son's trouble. Tell him not to speak my name when he is dying." Mr. Spider knew that Death would try to catch him if his name were spoken.

Mr. Spider left that village at once. He ran as fast as he could to a faraway place where he thought Death would not find him.

So it was that Madam Telu, the clever mother, managed to get what belonged to her. She showed her son that there are many better ways to get your property from the strong, and from a rascal, rather than fight for it.

GREEDY TURTLE SAT BENEATH THE CORKWOOD TREE,
CATCHING THE CHIPS

8: Greedy Turtle and the Blue-Wings

LONG ago there lived a turtle that always liked to eat. He ate so much and so often that other animals called him "Greedy Turtle."

In this land there grew a great corkwood tree. Many birds liked to eat the seeds of this tree. Strange as it may seem, the birds that ate the seeds of the corkwood had lovely blue feathers.

Greedy Turtle sat beneath the corkwood tree, catching the chips or outer hulls of the seeds as the birds cracked them open. For a time he was satisfied with the hulls of the seeds.

Then suddenly, he was not satisfied.

"Why should I be content to eat only the hulls

of the seeds? If I had wings I would eat the full seed as the birds do. I am as good as those birds. I should have wings, also."

So he asked Oldman God for wings.

"Why do you want wings?" Oldman God asked.

"I want wings so I can eat seeds from the tree as the birds do. I do not want to sit under the tree eating the hulls that the birds do not want. I want to eat equally with them."

Then Oldman God called the blue-winged birds and asked them to help Greedy Turtle.

"Each of you give the turtle one of your feathers," Oldman God commanded. "Then he will be happy."

The birds did as God asked them to do.

The next day the blue-wings went to the corkwood to eat the seeds as usual. Along with them came Greedy Turtle, spreading his new blue wings wide and proud.

Greedy Turtle flew at once to the very best branches and began to eat the seeds as fast as he could. Worse than that, he did not even allow the blue-winged birds to come near the good branches.

The blue-wings became very angry and began to talk among themselves.

"Is not this fellow the same one we helped yesterday?" asked one.

"WHY DO YOU WANT WINGS?" OLDMAN GOD ASKED

"It is the same," another answered. "We each gave him a feather so that now he has these fine blue wings, and see how he acts!"

"It was Oldman God who asked us to give this greedy creature feathers," said the first blue-wing. "Let us now complain to Oldman God and ask Him what we can do."

So they went to Oldman God, and one blue-wing said, "Oldman, that creature you told us to help so he could eat with us has driven us from the fine branches of the corkwood tree. He spreads his borrowed wings over the best seeds and will not let us come near. What can we do so that we may have enough food again?"

Oldman God sent for Greedy Turtle and questioned him. Greedy Turtle denied the charge against him.

Oldman God, the Almighty, knowing all things that happen, did not argue with Greedy Turtle. He knew what was going on between the birds and Greedy Turtle. He told the birds to go back to the good branches of the corkwood tree and to continue eating the seeds as before. Then Oldman God gave them one more bit of advice.

"If Greedy Turtle does the same thing again, each of you should pluck a feather from his wings."

On the first and second day after Oldman God

had thus advised the blue-wings, all went well. Greedy Turtle behaved himself. He and the birds ate together in peace, and all had as much as they needed.

But certain things are true about all creatures. A leopard never loses his spots, never forgets the ways of a leopard; nor does a lion forget how to make a noise loud enough to shake the jungle. It is sometimes hard to get rid of a way of doing something which is born into one.

On the third day Greedy Turtle began to behave as usual. He spread his wings wide and did not allow the birds near the best seeds, thus causing them to go hungry.

The birds then did as Oldman God had advised. They flew at Greedy Turtle, each bird picking one feather from his wings.

Greedy Turtle fell on the earth with a big sound!

Since that day Greedy Turtle never goes any further than the paths near his own living places. He must always walk slowly beneath the trees and at the base of the mountains.

GBAN SAT THERE, GAPING AND LICKING HIS MOUTH

9: The Hated Dog Gban

IN a crowded village of fishermen there lived a frisky dog called Gban. Gban was fond of picking and stealing people's fish and meat from their hiding places. The people hated Gban and used abusive and vulgar language against him in public.

Even though Gban did all these things, he was not aware of his unbecoming actions. He wondered why people hated him. He went to a fortune teller named Dermy to discover the cause of all the noises against him.

The fortune teller left Gban sitting inside and went outdoors to urinate. Near Gban were the fortune teller's detective instruments: fat bones, meat, and fried crawfish. Gban looked through the keyhole and saw no one. At once he broke the bones, ate the sweet marrow, and licked the spot where the instruments had been lying.

Dermy returned and saw that his detective instruments were missing. Gban sat there, gaping and licking his mouth, and Dermy knew what had happened but he took it like a man. He sat down quietly and said to Gban:

"Lo, I have no instruments to detect your case. You have swallowed the bones and the meat I need to do your work."

The dog could not say a word. He was ashamed and turned his back to the fortune teller.

"Hail! Turn your face to me, Gban," said the fortune teller. "In this world," he continued, "no one is responsible for the riches and good name of any man. Man, like a magnet, draws people to himself through goodwill. But you have no regard for the property of others. Nobody is against you, it is you who cause trouble for yourself—you, you, you. From now on, keep away from other peoples' belongings. Then you will prosper and have many friends."

GUINEA HEN CARES FOR HER EGGS UNDER THE
CORKWOOD TREE

10: Guinea Hen's Children

GUINEA Hen made her nest under the great corkwood tree at the edge of the rain forest. The storms of May would soon be coming, for the rainy season was about to begin.

But Guinea Hen knew all about this. She knew she would be sitting on her eggs for many days to keep them warm, and she was ready to suffer in this way.

She cared for her six eggs well, as she must do to bring them to hatching time. Many discomforts came to her, but she stayed patiently on her nest. Snakes crawled over her, chop time passed her. She waited without taking any exercise, for she did not dare to leave her nest.

In all this, she held the hope that some day her children would help her.

At last the day came when she knew the eggs were ready to hatch. Each was full of its own young guinea. It was time to question each coming child about its life plans.

She picked one egg and asked it by name, "Co-Co, what would you do for me, my child, if I hatch you?"

"I shall seek for a better forest where we could get more termites for our daily food," said Co-Co.

She laid it aside and asked another, "Ky-Ky, what about you? What will you do for me?"

A small voice from inside the egg replied, "I shall be watchful whenever we are on the hunt for food so that we may not enter a trap or cause snakes to be angry."

Another small voice promised to bring plenty of common sea salt to her from Monrovia.

She asked five of the eggs this same question, and all five promised to make some good return for the sake of their little and simple life on earth.

The last one to be questioned was Fo-Fo, who said, "I shall be by myself, and I will go all over the forest for my own sake and as I please. Your mother bore you and that was a debt against you. Now, your having me should be the payment of the debt you owe my grandparents. Please expect nothing from me!"

When Guinea Hen heard this cross and ungrateful statement from Fo-Fo, she felt very sad and somewhat angry as well. So Guinea Hen hatched the first five good eggs and left Fo-Fo in the shell. She did not even cover the shell.

Guinea Hen and the five newly hatched guinea children moved on to a faraway forest. They forgot about Fo-Fo, the intended vagabond.

The very next noontime after Guinea Hen had left with her new children a rain came with a heavy storm. The wind was so strong that it broke a little branch of the corkwood which sheltered Fo-Fo who was still inside the egg.

This cracked the egg and allowed Fo-Fo to get out. Once Fo-Fo was out of the egg he realized who he was. He knew he had a mother, sisters, and brothers. Now he must find them.

Day after day and night after night he went looking for his family. He shouted and cried for his mother with no good result. Now and then a woods creature sympathized with him and sometimes even offered to help him hunt.

But Fo-Fo could never accept these offers with kindness or appreciation. He would say something like, "How can you help me? You do not know my mother or any of my family. Such a one as you can be of no help to me."

After such a reply as this the sympathizer would change his manners and usually answer in cross words.

One day a snail saw Fo-Fo and said, "Son, come this way and lodge with me. I am your mother."

But Fo-Fo said, "Keep your goodness with you. Don't you see the different ways we walk? You are not made at all like me. You are not my mother. Our family never walks as you do, leaving a messy trail behind them. Please let me pass!"

A bittern in its swampy home heard him crying and called, "Fo-Fo, Fo-Fo!"

Fo-Fo had an impatient answer for the bittern also.

"Keep your hissing noises in your mouth, you long-footed one!" he said.

Fo-Fo continued on his way, searching for his mother, crossly refusing any sympathy or help. At last he came to the place where his mother and others in his family were busily finding their food.

Guinea Hen saw her son coming, but she did not call out to him. She poured some termites near a hidden trap.

Fo-Fo had been hungry for a long time. He

was so hungry that his eyes became watery and he had no strength or vision to look for food beyond this place.

He made a grab for the pile of termites and instantly the trap caught him and lifted him off his feet. There he hung, dangling in the air, with his feet in the trap which had been set by his own mother for his ungratefulness to her.

This unusual happening between Ma and Son took place because the son forgot that when he was growing in his mother's egg he was never cold, never wet with rain, never hurt from the outside. He was fed from the egg, which had first been a part of his mother's body.

Fo-Fo learned that we must reap what we sow. Fo-Fo now hangs, while ants struggle to reach him.

FO-FO—THERE HE HUNG, DANGLING IN THE AIR, WITH HIS
FEET IN THE TRAP

Some Proverbs

Fish knows what type of hairy caterpillar to swallow.

(Every man knows where to play pranks or practice his crooked ways.)

Water Deer says, "It is better to carry a scar than to be found in palm-butter soup."

(It is better to be alive and have problems than dead and have no problems.)

He is like a bird that is without a farm, yet has a full stomach all day.

(Although he has no visible means of support, the lucky guy seems never to go hungry.)

You must first catch the lizard before asking Auntie if one can kill lizards on her farm.

(Don't boast of a thing until you know you can do it.)

A stranger at a table with palm-butter rice never cares to know how much crops the farm yields.

(Most people never think of someone else's problems if they are enjoying themselves.)

He who is not sleepy usually complains of the bed being dirty.

(If one does not want to do a thing, he finds small excuses.)

Apples are for monkeys, but when the monkeys don't know how to manage, the apples fall on the ground for the deer.

(Stupid people usually miss their good luck.)

One who has already fallen into the water should not worry about getting his trousers wet.

(Worry about how you will get out of the trouble, not how you got into it.)

If a dog is praised for hunting, he is likely to hunt for leopard.

(Too much praising makes some people try to do things beyond their abilities.)

The foot that travels usually brings something home.

(One who visits places must bring home something, either goods or wisdom.)

About the Author

PETER G. DORLIAE is a Paramount Chief of the Yarwin-Mehnsonoh Chiefdom, Lower Nimba County, Liberia. In 1958 he was graduated from Saint Patrick's High School, Monrovia, and then he attended the University of Liberia for two years.

In 1966, after the death of his father, Paramount Chief Weh Dorliae, Peter Dorliae was for three years acting paramount chief. In the general elections of 1968, he defeated three other candidates at the polls and was himself elected.

Mr. Dorliae lives in the town of Mehnla, where he was born. He also has an official address in Monrovia.

About the Artist

S. I. WANGBOJE, Nigerian artist-teacher, completed his doctorate at New York University in New York City and is now a research fellow in art at the University of Ife. Dr. Wangboje lives with his wife and children in Ife, Nigeria.

68